Andrew Brodie Basics
LET'S DO ADDITION AND SUBTRACTION

FOR AGES 5-6

with over **100** reward stickers

- Over 400 practice questions
- Regular progress tests
- Extra quick-fire questions and handy tips

Published 2016 by Bloomsbury Publishing Plc
50 Bedford Square, London, WC1B 3DP

www.bloomsbury.com

ISBN 978-14729-2618-0

Copyright © 2016 Bloomsbury Publishing
Text copyright © 2016 Andrew Brodie
Cover and inside illustrations of Pippa the Penguin and Andrew Brodie
© 2016 Nikalas Catlow. Other inside illustrations © 2016 Cathy Hughes

A CIP catalogue for this book is available from the British Library.

10 9 8 7 6 5 4 3 2 1

Printed in China by Leo Paper Products

This book is produced using paper that is made from wood grown in managed,
sustainable forests. It is natural, renewable and recyclable. The logging and manufacturing
processes conform to the environmental regulations of the country of origin.

To see our full range of titles visit www.bloomsbury.com

BLOOMSBURY

Introduction

This is the first in the series of Andrew Brodie *Let's Do Addition and Subtraction* books. The book contains more than 400 mental maths questions, deliberately designed to cover the following key aspects of the 'Number' section of the National Curriculum:

- Number and place value
- Addition and subtraction

Your child will benefit most greatly if you have the opportunity to discuss the questions with them. You may find that your child gains low scores when they first begin to take the tests. Make sure that they don't lose confidence: instead, encourage them to learn from their mistakes.

The level of difficulty increases gradually throughout the book, but note that some questions are repeated. This is to ensure that pupils have the opportunity to learn vital new facts: they may not know the answer to a particular question the first time they encounter it, but this provides the opportunity for you to help them to learn it for the next time that they come across it. Don't be surprised if they need to practise certain questions many times.

In Year 1, pupils are introduced to a wide range of new mathematical vocabulary. In relation to addition, the children need to learn the use of expressions such as 'put together', 'add', 'altogether', 'total' and 'more than'. For subtraction, they need to learn 'take away', 'distance between', 'difference between' and 'less than'. The activities in this book will encourage children to start using this mathematical language.

It is also important that children learn to understand and use mathematical sentences, appreciating the meanings of the addition, subtraction and equals signs, and relating these to the vocabulary that they have learnt.

Children gain confidence by learning facts that they can use in their future work. With lots of practice they will see their score improve and will learn to find maths both satisfying and enjoyable.

Look out for...

Pippa the Penguin, who provides useful tips and helpful advice.

Brodie's Fast Five, quick-fire questions designed to test your child's mental arithmetic.

Lots of additions

You can use your fingers for some questions if you want to.

1 How many cats?  **3** cats

How many cats? **2** cats

How many cats are there altogether? $5 + 2 =$ **7**

2 1 more than 7 = **8**

3 1 more than 10 = **11**

4 Add together four and three. $4 + 3 =$

5 $1 + 1 =$ **2**

6 $2 + 1 =$ **3**

7 $3 + 1 =$ **4**

8 $4 + 1 =$ **5**

9 $5 + 1 =$ **6**

10 $6 + 1 =$ **7**

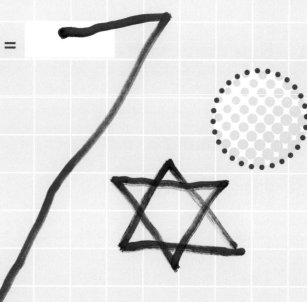

Brodie's Fast Five

$6 + 2 =$ **8** ✓	$3 + 4 =$ **7**
$7 + 1 =$ **8** ✗	$5 + 3 =$ **9** $10 + 1 =$ **11**

Lots of subtractions

Remember, you can use your fingers for some questions if it helps.

1   How many birds are on the bird table?   birds

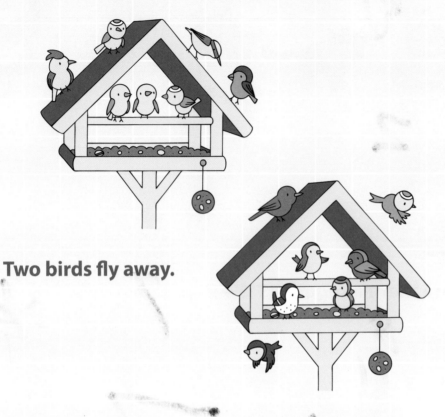

Two birds fly away.

How many birds are on the bird table now?   birds

7 – 2 =

2   1 less than 7 =

3   1 less than 10 =

4   Take three away from five.   5 – 3 =

5   10 – 1 =

6   9 – 1 =

7   8 – 1 =

8   7 – 1 =

9   6 – 1 =

10   5 – 1 =

Addition problems

1

There are six bricks on the table. Faye collects two more bricks.

How many bricks are there altogether? [   ] **bricks**

six bricks + two bricks = eight bricks

$$6 + 2 = 8$$

2

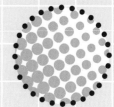

There are seven birds on the bird table. Two more birds arrive.

How many birds are there altogether? [   ] **bricks**

Complete the sentence below about the birds, then complete the addition sentence.

[   ]   **birds +** [   ]   **birds =** [   ]   **birds**

[   ]   **+** [   ]   **=**

The addition sentence in question 1 is 8 – 2 = 6.

1 **There are eight cars in the car park.**

Two cars leave.

How many cars are there now?   **cars**

8 cars – 2 cars = 6 cars

8 – 2 = 6

2

There are nine peas in the pod.

Harry eats three of the peas.

How many peas are left in the pod?   **peas**

Complete the sentence below, and then complete the subtraction sentence.

     peas –   peas   =   peas

     –   =

Brodie's Fast Five

7 – 4 =   10 – 5 =

6 – 6 =   12 – 3 =   9 – 8 =

Addition and subtraction

Remember to look closely at which sign is used.

This is the addition sign. ✚   This is the subtraction sign. ▬

1   7 + 2 =

2   1 more than 9 =

3   1 less than 6 =

4   Add together five and five.   5 + 5 =

5   Take three away from nine.   9 − 3 =

6   What is the total of eight and two?   8 + 2 =

7   What is seven take away four?   7 − 4 =

8   Here are seven stars. Draw three more stars.

How many stars are there altogether now?   stars

Write the addition sentence about the stars.

     +   =

9   10 − 7 =

10   10 − 3 =

Brodie's Fast Five

9 − 4 =   8 − 3 =

7 − 2 =   6 − 1 =   10 − 5 =

Addition

1 6 + 2 =

2 8 + 4 =

3 0 + 7 =

4 5 + 5 =

5 9 + 3 =

Subtraction

6 8 − 1 =

7 9 − 5 =

8 10 − 1 =

9 6 − 0 =

10 5 − 4 =

11

There are nine cars in the car park.

Two cars leave.

Complete the sentence below, and then complete the subtraction sentence.

cars −   cars =   cars

−   =

12 Here are five stars. Draw four more stars.

How many stars are there altogether now?

Write the addition sentence about the stars.

+   =

Lots of additions

1 How many hats? ⬚ hats

How many hats? ⬚ hats

How many hats are there altogether? ⬚ hats

Write the addition sentence for the hats.

⬚ + ⬚ = ⬚

2 1 more than 12 =

3 1 more than 23 =

4 Add together seven and six. $7 + 6 =$

5 $7 + 2 =$

6 $8 + 2 =$

7 $9 + 2 =$

8 $10 + 2 =$

9 $11 + 2 =$

10 $12 + 2 =$

> You can use counters or other objects to help you with some questions if you want to.

Brodie's Fast Five

$7 + 5 =$ $8 + 4 =$

$6 + 6 =$ $9 + 3 =$ $10 + 2 =$

Lots of subtractions

Remember, you can use counters or other objects to help you with some questions.

1 How many biscuits are there? [   ] biscuits

Amy ate two biscuits.

How many biscuits are there now? [   ] biscuits

Write the subtraction sentence for the biscuits.

[   ] – [   ] =

2 1 less than 12 =

3 1 less than 18 =

4 Take six away from eleven. 11 – 6 =

5 13 – 2 =

6 9 – 2 =

7 14 – 2 =

8 16 – 2 =

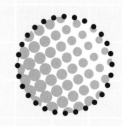

9 2 – 2 =

10 15 – 2 =

Brodie's Fast Five

10 – 2 = [   ]   17 – 1 = [   ]

11 – 3 = [   ]   12 – 2 = [   ]   10 – 4 = [   ]

Let's make ten

There are lots of ways you can make ten by adding different numbers together.

Look: $8 + 2 = 10$
         $2 + 8 = 10$

Write all the ways of making ten by adding whole numbers. One is done for you.

$0 + 10$

10

Write out all the number bonds that make ten by adding two whole numbers together. One is done for you.

$2 + 8 = 10$

Brodie's Fast Five

$12 + 2 =$ ⬚ $13 + 2 =$ ⬚

$11 + 4 =$ ⬚ $9 + 6 =$ ⬚ $10 + 9 =$ ⬚

Let's make two

Use subtractions to find two.

Here are some subtractions that make two.

$8 - 6 = 2$

$9 - 7 = 2$

For the next activity you are only allowed to use the numbers below.
You can use each number more than once if you want to.

0 1 2 3 4 5 6 7 8 9 10

Using these numbers, try to find subtractions that make two.
One is done for you.

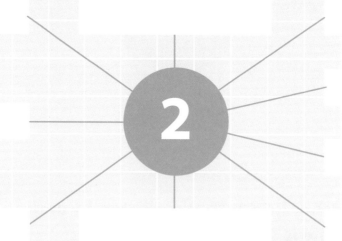

7 – 5

2

Write out all the subtraction facts you have found that make two.
One is done for you.

5 – 3 = 2

Brodie's Fast Five

12 – 4 =   13 – 5 =

11 – 11 =   12 – 9 =   15 – 3 =

Addition and subtraction

Read the questions carefully to check whether they are additions or subtractions.

This is the addition sign. **+**   This is the subtraction sign. **—**

1   14 + 2 =

2   1 more than 19 =

3   1 less than 21 =

4   Add together eight and eight. 8 + 8 =

5   Take three away from twenty. 20 – 3 =

6   What is the total of eighteen and two? 18 + 2 =

7   What is sixteen take away four? 16 – 4 =

8   10 – 6 =

9   10 + 6 =

10   Find ways of making seven by adding two whole numbers together. One is done for you.

0 + 7

7

Brodie's Fast Five

19 – 4 =   18 – 3 =

17 – 2 =   16 – 1 =   20 – 5 =

Addition

1 9 + 5 =

2 8 + 7 =

3 10 + 7 =

4 15 + 5 =

5 19 + 1 =

Subtraction

6 20 − 1 =

7 15 − 5 =

8 14 − 5 =

9 20 − 0 =

10 20 − 4 =

11 Find ways of making nine by adding pairs of numbers together.

Write all the ways of making nine by adding whole numbers. One is done for you.

6 + 3

Write out all the number bonds that make nine. One is done for you.

2 + 7 = 9

12 0 1 2 3 4 5 6 7 8 9 10

Using these numbers, try to find subtractions that make three. One is done for you.

10 − 7

Write out all the subtraction facts that you have found to make three. One is done for you.

7 − 4 = 3

Adding using number lines

Number lines can help a lot with adding.

Look at this number line. We start on six and add three to get to nine.

Start on 6   Jump forward 3

The addition sentence for this number line is $6 + 3 = 9$

Write the addition sentence for each number line below.

Brodie's Fast Five

$7 + 7 =$

$8 + 8 =$

$6 + 6 =$

$9 + 9 =$

$10 + 10 =$

Subtracting using number lines

Number lines can help a lot with subtracting.

Look at this number line. We start on eight and subtract three to get to five.

Jump back 3   Start on 8

The subtraction sentence for this number line is 8 – 3 = 5

Write the subtraction sentence for each number line below.

Brodie's Fast Five

10 – 5 =

18 – 1 =

15 – 3 =

20 – 2 =

19 – 4 =

Let's make twelve

There are lots of ways to make twelve by adding different numbers together.

Look: 10 + 2 = 12
2 + 10 = 12

Write all the ways of making twelve by adding two whole numbers together. One is done for you.

0 + 12

12

Write out all the number bonds that make twelve. One is done for you.

3 + 9 = 12

Brodie's Fast Five

18 + 2 =

14 + 5 =

11 + 7 =

9 + 8 =

10 + 6 =

Let's make three

How many subtraction bonds can you find that make three?

Here are some subtractions that make three.

$9 - 6 = 3$

$12 - 9 = 3$

For the next activity you are only allowed to use the numbers below. You can use each number more than once if you want to.

0 1 2 3 4 5 6 7 8 9 10 11 12

Using these numbers, try to find subtractions that make three. One is done for you.

3 – 0

Write out all the subtraction facts that you have found to make three. One is done for you.

11 – 8 = 3

Brodie's Fast Five

20 – 4 =   20 – 8 =

20 – 11 =   20 – 9 =   20 – 3 =

Addition and subtraction

Some special words tell you to add and some tell you to subtract.

These are addition words:

put together   add   altogether   total   more than

These are subtraction words:

take away   distance between   difference between   less than

1. **Put together seven and four.** $7 + 4 =$

2. **3 more than 17 =**

3. **3 less than 15 =**

4. **Add together ten and ten.** $10 + 10 =$

5. **What is sixteen take away nine?** $16 - 9 =$

6. **What is the total of twenty and five?** $20 + 5 =$

7. **What is the difference between twelve and nineteen?** $19 - 12 =$

8. **How much altogether is fourteen and nine?** $14 + 9 =$

9. **How much less than twenty is seventeen?** $20 - 17 =$

10. **Find ways of making eight by adding pairs of numbers together.**

$2 + 6$

8

Brodie's Fast Five

$21 - 4 =$ $20 - 3 =$

$15 - 2 =$ $20 - 1 =$ $14 - 5 =$

Addition

1 $9 + 8 =$

2 $12 + 7 =$

3 $10 + 10 =$

4 $15 + 6 =$

5 $19 + 4 =$

Subtraction

6 $20 - 8 =$

7 $22 - 5 =$

8 $21 - 6 =$

9 $20 - 11 =$

10 $23 - 4 =$

11 Write the addition sentence for each number line.

12 Write the subtraction sentence for each number line.

Adding using number lines

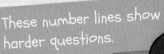
These number lines show harder questions.

Write the addition sentence for each number line.

0 1 2 3 4 5 6 7 8 9 10 11 12 13 14 15 16 17 18 19 20

0 1 2 3 4 5 6 7 8 9 10 11 12 13 14 15 16 17 18 19 20

0 1 2 3 4 5 6 7 8 9 10 11 12 13 14 15 16 17 18 19 20

0 1 2 3 4 5 6 7 8 9 10 11 12 13 14 15 16 17 18 19 20

0 1 2 3 4 5 6 7 8 9 10 11 12 13 14 15 16 17 18 19 20

0 1 2 3 4 5 6 7 8 9 10 11 12 13 14 15 16 17 18 19 20

0 1 2 3 4 5 6 7 8 9 10 11 12 13 14 15 16 17 18 19 20

0 1 2 3 4 5 6 7 8 9 10 11 12 13 14 15 16 17 18 19 20

Brodie's Fast Five

$7 + 7 =$ $\qquad$ $12 + 5 =$

$14 + 6 =$ $\qquad$ $15 + 5 =$ $\qquad$ $6 + 10 =$

Subtracting using number lines

These number lines show harder subtractions.

Write the subtraction sentence for each number line.

0 1 2 3 4 5 6 7 8 9 10 11 12 13 14 15 16 17 18 19 20

0 1 2 3 4 5 6 7 8 9 10 11 12 13 14 15 16 17 18 19 20

0 1 2 3 4 5 6 7 8 9 10 11 12 13 14 15 16 17 18 19 20

0 1 2 3 4 5 6 7 8 9 10 11 12 13 14 15 16 17 18 19 20

0 1 2 3 4 5 6 7 8 9 10 11 12 13 14 15 16 17 18 19 20

0 1 2 3 4 5 6 7 8 9 10 11 12 13 14 15 16 17 18 19 20

0 1 2 3 4 5 6 7 8 9 10 11 12 13 14 15 16 17 18 19 20

0 1 2 3 4 5 6 7 8 9 10 11 12 13 14 15 16 17 18 19 20

Brodie's Fast Five

20 − 3 = 18 − 7 =

19 − 5 = 20 − 8 = 17 − 8 =

Let's make thirteen

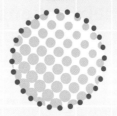
There are lots of ways to make thirteen by adding.

Look: $10 + 3 = 13$
$3 + 10 = 13$

Write all the ways of making thirteen by adding whole numbers. One is done for you.

4 + 9

13

Write out all the number bonds that make thirteen. One is done for you.

4 + 9 = 13

Brodie's Fast Five

3 + 12 =   4 + 15 =

7 + 8 =   6 + 11 =   8 + 12 =

23

Let's make four

How many subtractions can you think of that make the number four?

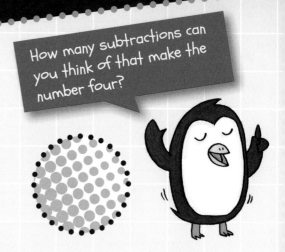

Here are some subtractions that make four.

$12 - 8 = 4$
$14 - 10 = 4$

For the next activity you are only allowed to use the numbers below.
You can use each number more than once if you want to.

0 1 2 3 4 5 6 7 8 9 10 11 12 13 14

Using these numbers, try to find subtractions that make four.
One is done for you.

10 - 6

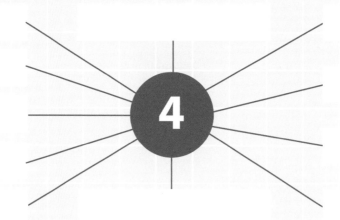

4

Write out all the subtraction facts you have found to make four.
One is done for you.

13 - 9 = 4

Brodie's Fast Five

$20 - 7 =$ 　　　　 $20 - 12 =$

$20 - 6 =$ 　　　　 $20 - 11 =$ 　　　　 $20 - 4 =$

24

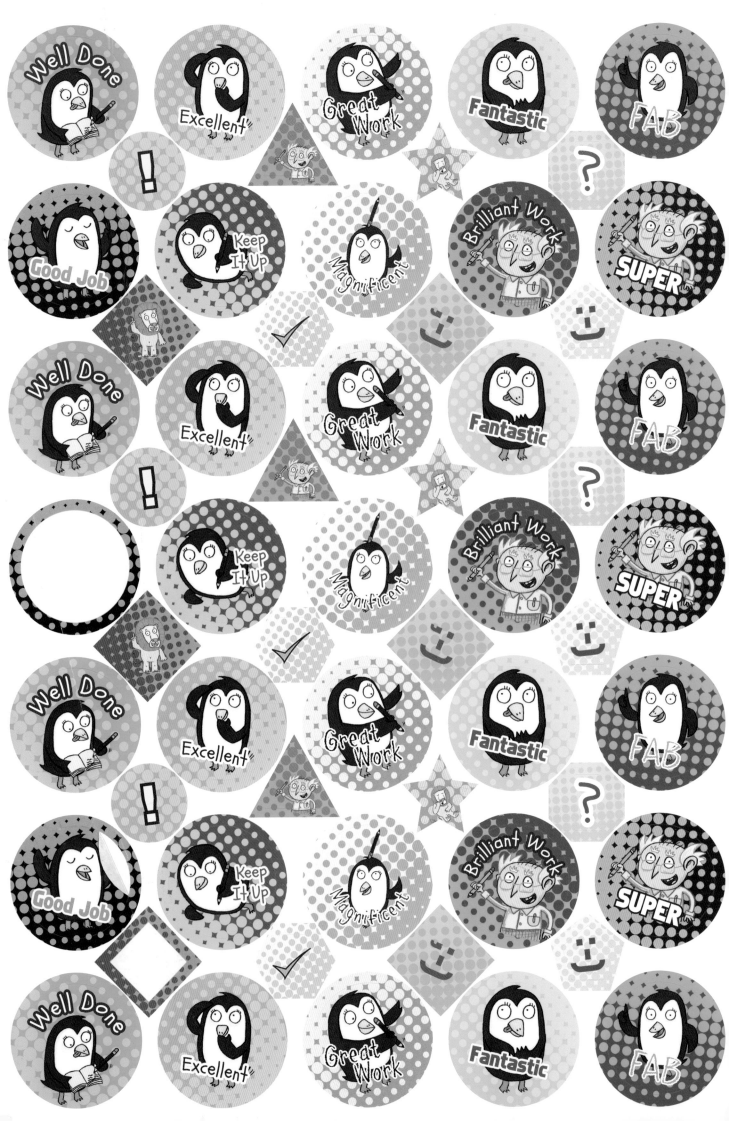

Addition and subtraction

Can you remember which words tell you to add and which tell you to subtract?

1. Put together eight and six. 8 + 6 =

2. 3 more than 15 =

3. 3 less than 17 =

4. Add together six and seven. 6 + 7 =

5. What is fifteen take away nine? 15 – 9 =

6. What is the total of twelve and five? 12 + 5 =

7. What is the difference between seventeen and eleven?

   17 – 11 =

8. How much altogether is eight and nine? 8 + 9 =

9. How much less than twenty is thirteen? 20 – 13 =

10. Find ways of making eleven by adding pairs of numbers together.

2 + 9

11

Brodie's Fast Five

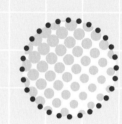

19 – 4 =   11 – 3 =

17 – 2 =   20 – 11 =   13 – 5 =

Look carefully at the addition or subtraction sign in each question.

1 $7 + 8 =$

2 $12 - 7 =$

3 $10 + 9 =$

4 $15 - 6 =$

5 $7 + 4 =$

6 $20 - 9 =$

7 $12 + 4 =$

8 $17 - 6 =$

9 $18 + 2 =$

10 $20 - 14 =$

11 Write the addition sentence for each number line.

12 Write the subtraction sentence for each number line.

Adding to find missing numbers

Can you count on to find the answers to these questions?

Can you find the missing numbers?
You can use counters to help you, or you may find the number line below helpful.

0 1 2 3 4 5 6 7 8 9 10 11 12 13 14 15 16 17 18 19 20

1 6 + ☐ = 10

2 3 + ☐ = 10

3 9 + ☐ = 10

4 2 + ☐ = 10

5 4 + ☐ = 10

6 1 + ☐ = 10

7 5 + ☐ = 10

8 8 + ☐ = 10

9 7 + ☐ = 10

10 0 + ☐ = 10

Brodie's Fast Five

8 + 6 = ☐   12 + 7 = ☐

11 + 6 = ☐   13 + 5 = ☐   6 + 9 = ☐

27

Subtracting to find missing numbers

Can you count back to find the answers to these questions?

Can you find the missing numbers?
You can use counters to help you, or you may find the number line below helpful.

0 – 1 – 2 – 3 – 4 – 5 – 6 – 7 – 8 – 9 – 10 – 11 – 12 – 13 – 14 – 15 – 16 – 17 – 18 – 19 – 20

1   10 –   = 3

2   10 –   = 9

3   10 –   = 1

4   10 –   = 10

5   10 –   = 6

6   10 –   = 7

7   10 –   = 2

8   10 –   = 4

9   10 –   = 0

10   10 –   = 5

Brodie's Fast Five

20 – 4 =   17 – 7 =

19 – 12 =   20 – 15 =   17 – 11 =

Let's make fourteen

There are lots of ways to make fourteen by adding.

Look: 9 + 5 = 14
5 + 9 = 14

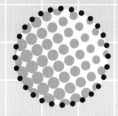

Write down all the ways of making fourteen by adding whole numbers. One is done for you.

7 + 7

14

Write out all the number bonds that make fourteen. One is done for you.

2 + 12 = 14

Brodie's Fast Five

6 + 12 =   5 + 15 =

17 + 2 =   12 + 7 =   13 + 6 =

Let's make five

How many subtractions can you think of that make the number five?

Here are some subtractions that make five.

$$14 - 9 = 5$$
$$11 - 6 = 5$$

For the next activity you are only allowed to use the numbers below.
You can use each number more than once if you want to.

0 1 2 3 4 5 6 7 8 9 10 11 12 13 14 15

Using these numbers, try to find subtractions that make five.
One is done for you.

9 - 4 = 5

5

Write out all the subtraction bonds that you have found to make five.
One is done for you.

11 - 6 = 5

Brodie's Fast Five

20 – 13 = 　　　　　20 – 9 =

20 – 12 = 　　　　　20 – 8 = 　　　　　20 – 5 =

Addition and subtraction

Can you remember which words tell you to add and which tell you to subtract?

Write the number sentence for each question.

1. Put together seven and six.

2. What is five more than twelve? =

3. What is four less than fifteen? =

4. Add together eight and seven.

5. What is eighteen take away twelve?

6. What is the total of thirteen and five?

7. What is the difference between twenty and eleven?

8. How much altogether is seven and nine?

9. How much less than twenty is twelve?

10. For this question you are only allowed to use the numbers below. You can use each number more than once if you want to.

0 1 2 3 4 5 6 7 8 9 10 11 12 13 14 15

Using these numbers, try to find lots of subtractions that make six. One is done for you.

11 − 5

6

Brodie's Fast Five

4 − 4 =

16 − 3 =

17 − 12 =

20 − 13 =

13 − 9 =

Look carefully at the addition or subtraction sign in each question.

1 $7 +$ $= 12$

2 $4 +$ $= 12$

3 $2 +$ $= 12$

4 $5 +$ $= 12$

5 $9 +$ $= 12$

6 $10 -$ $= 6$

7 $10 -$ $= 9$

8 $10 -$ $= 3$

9 $10 -$ $= 8$

10 $10 -$ $= 2$

Write the number sentence for each question.

11 Put together fourteen and six.

12 What is eight more than seven? =

13 What is nine less than sixteen? =

14 Add together nine and six.

15 What is sixteen take away nine?

16 What is the total of sixteen and four?

17 What is the difference between twenty and eight?

18 How much altogether is six and five?

Adding to find missing numbers

Can you count on to find the answers to these questions?

Can you find the missing numbers?
You can use counters to help you, or you
may find the number line below helpful.

0 · 1 · 2 · 3 · 4 · 5 · 6 · 7 · 8 · 9 · 10 · 11 · 12 · 13 · 14 · 15 · 16 · 17 · 18 · 19 · 20

1 ____ + 4 = 11

2 ____ + 9 = 11

3 ____ + 5 = 11

4 ____ + 10 = 11

5 ____ + 0 = 11

6 ____ + 6 = 11

7 ____ + 11 = 11

8 ____ + 3 = 11

9 ____ + 7 = 11

10 ____ + 8 = 11

Brodie's Fast Five

18 + 2 = ____   12 + 8 = ____

11 + 4 = ____   10 + 7 = ____   11 + 9 = ____

Subtracting to find missing numbers

Can you count back to find the answers to these questions?

Can you find the missing numbers?
You can use counters to help you, or you may find the number line below helpful.

(0)-(1)-(2)-(3)-(4)-(5)-(6)-(7)-(8)-(9)-(10)-(11)-(12)-(13)-(14)-(15)-(16)-(17)-(18)-(19)-(20)

1 ___ − 6 = 5

2 ___ − 7 = 3

3 ___ − 2 = 9

4 ___ − 4 = 7

5 ___ − 5 = 4

6 ___ − 8 = 6

7 ___ − 1 = 9

8 ___ − 6 = 13

9 ___ − 4 = 15

10 ___ − 8 = 12

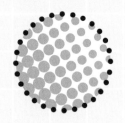

Brodie's Fast Five

20 − 16 = ___   19 − 4 = ___

17 − 8 = ___   18 − 15 = ___   16 − 3 = ___

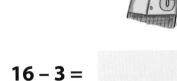

Let's make fifteen

There are lots of ways to make fifteen by adding.

Look: 10 + 5 = 15
5 + 10 = 15

Write all the ways of making fifteen by adding whole numbers. One is done for you.

9 + 6

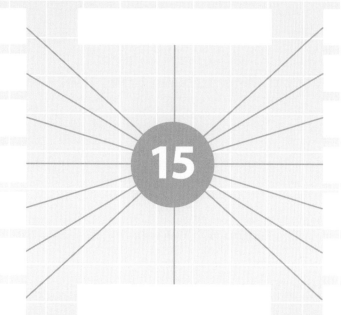

15

Write out all the number bonds that make fifteen. One is done for you.

2 + 13 = 15

Brodie's Fast Five

7 + 9 =

8 + 8 =

14 + 3 =

11 + 8 =

9 + 9 =

Let's make six

How many subtractions can you think of that make the number six?

Here are some subtractions that make six.

$$14 - 8 = 6$$
$$10 - 4 = 6$$

For the next activity you are only allowed to use the numbers below.
You can use each number more than once if you want to.

0 1 2 3 4 5 6 7 8 9 10 11 12 13 14 15 16

Using these numbers, try to find subtractions that make six.
One is done for you.

17 - 11

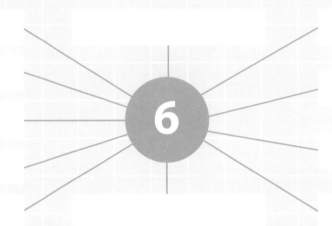

Write out all the subtraction facts that you have found to make six.
One is done for you.

15 - 9 = 6

Brodie's Fast Five

20 – 11 = ☐   20 – 6 = ☐

20 – 14 = ☐   20 – 18 = ☐   20 – 15 = ☐

Addition and subtraction

Can you remember which words tell you to add and which tell you to subtract?

Write the number sentence for each question.

1 Put together twelve and four.

2 What is eight more than twelve? =

3 What is eight less than fifteen? =

4 Add together nine and three.

5 What is nineteen take away twelve?

6 What is the total of seventeen and three?

7 What is the difference between twenty and thirteen?

8 How much altogether is six and eight?

9 How much less than twenty is two?

10 For this question you are only allowed to use the numbers below. You can use each number more than once if you want to.

0 1 2 3 4 5 6 7 8 9 10 11 12 13 14 15 16 17

Using these numbers, try to find subtractions that make seven. One is done for you.

12 − 5

Brodie's Fast Five

14 − 4 =   16 − 15 =

17 − 1 =   20 − 18 =   14 − 5 =

Find the missing number in each question.

1	+ 7 = 12
2	+ 8 = 12
3	+ 5 = 12
4	+ 10 = 12
5	+ 11 = 12
6	− 8 = 12
7	− 1 = 19
8	− 3 = 11
9	− 7 = 10
10	− 2 = 16

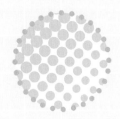

Write the number sentence for each question.

11 Put together twelve and five.

12 What is nine more than eight? =

13 What is five less than sexteen? =

14 Add together eight and eleven.

15 What is twenty take away nine?

16 What is the total of fourteen and four?

17 What is the difference between seventeen and eight?

18 How much altogether is nine and five?

Adding one to any number

Use this number line to help you answer each question.

(1)–(2)–(3)–(4)–(5)–(6)–(7)–(8)–(9)–(10)
(11)–(12)–(13)–(14)–(15)–(16)–(17)–(18)–(19)–(20)
(21)–(22)–(23)–(24)–(25)–(26)–(27)–(28)–(29)–(30)
(31)–(32)–(33)–(34)–(35)–(36)–(37)–(38)–(39)–(40)
(41)–(42)–(43)–(44)–(45)–(46)–(47)–(48)–(49)–(50)

1   9 + 1 =

2   19 + 1 =

3   29 + 1 =

4   39 + 1 =

5   49 + 1 =

6   59 + 1 =

7   69 + 1 =

8   79 + 1 =

9   89 + 1 =

10 99 + 1 =

11   + 1 = 23

12   + 1 = 47

13   + 1 = 51

14   + 1 = 82

15   + 1 = 89

16 1 +   = 60

17 1 +   = 98

18 1 +   = 76

19 1 +   = 44

20 1 +   = 55

Brodie's Fast Five

13 +   = 20   + 8 = 12

11 +   = 20   + 6 = 12   9 +   = 20

39

Use this number line to help you answer each question.

1	2	3	4	5	6	7	8	9	10
11	12	13	14	15	16	17	18	19	20
21	22	23	24	25	26	27	28	29	30
31	32	33	34	35	36	37	38	39	40
41	42	43	44	45	46	47	48	49	50

1. $10 - 1 =$

2. $80 - 1 =$

3. $30 - 1 =$

4. $70 - 1 =$

5. $100 - 1 =$

6. $20 - 1 =$

7. $60 - 1 =$

8. $90 - 1 =$

9. $40 - 1 =$

10. $50 - 1 =$

11. $- 1 = 67$

12. $- 1 = 82$

13. $- 1 = 49$

14. $- 1 = 28$

15. $- 1 = 91$

16. $- 1 = 53$

17. $- 1 = 74$

18. $- 1 = 55$

19. $- 1 = 96$

20. $- 1 = 40$

Brodie's Fast Five

$- 7 = 12$ $- 9 = 8$

$- 5 = 12$ $- 8 = 7$ $- 4 = 16$

40

 # Let's make sixteen

There are lots of ways to make sixteen by adding.

Look: 10 + 6 = 16
6 + 10 = 16

Write down all the ways of making sixteen by adding whole numbers. One is done for you.

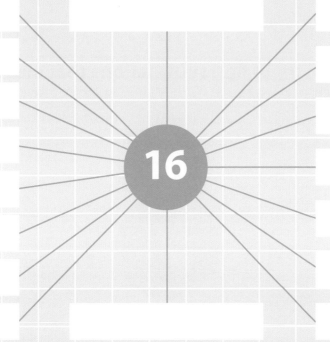

2 + 14

16

Write out all the number bonds that make sixteen. One is done for you.

15 + 1 = 16

Brodie's Fast Five

7 + [ ] = 16   [ ] + 3 = 16

2 + [ ] = 16   [ ] + 5 = 16   9 + [ ] = 16

Let's make seven

How many subtractions can you think of that make the number seven?

Here are some subtractions that make seven.

$15 - 8 = 7$
$11 - 4 = 7$

For the next activity you are only allowed to use the numbers below.
You can use each number more than once if you want to.

0 1 2 3 4 5 6 7 8 9 10 11 12 13 14 15 16 17

Using these numbers, try to find subtractions that make seven.
One is done for you.

12 – 5

Write out all the subtraction facts that you have found to make seven.
One is done for you.

15 – 8 = 7

Brodie's Fast Five

| 20 – | = 7 | | – 6 = 7 | |
| 14 – | = 7 | | – 9 = 7 | 18 – | = 7 |

Addition and subtraction

Additions and subtractions are related!

We know that $8 + 4 = 12$

This shows us that $12 - 8 = 4$

and $12 - 4 = 8$

Write the two subtraction sentences to go with each addition sentence.

1 $7 + 5 = 12$

2 $6 + 9 = 15$

3 $8 + 5 = 13$

4 $9 + 3 = 12$

5 $6 + 8 = 14$

6 $9 + 7 = 16$

Brodie's Fast Five

$14 - \boxed{} = 8$ $\boxed{} + 15 = 20$

$\boxed{} - 1 = 17$ $20 - \boxed{} = 3$ $\boxed{} - 5 = 7$

Answer these questions as fast as you can.

1	$53 + 1 =$		11	$30 - 1 =$
2	$68 + 1 =$		12	$70 - 1 =$
3	$75 + 1 =$		13	$100 - 1 =$
4	$+ 1 = 29$		14	$50 - 1 =$
5	$+ 1 = 60$		15	$80 - 1 =$
6	$+ 1 = 81$		16	$- 1 = 69$
7	$+ 1 = 77$		17	$- 1 = 52$
8	$1 + \quad = 90$		18	$- 1 = 73$
9	$1 + \quad = 28$		19	$- 1 = 88$
10	$1 + \quad = 34$		20	$- 1 = 90$

Complete the addition sentences, and then write two subtraction sentences to go with each.

21 $9 + 3 =$ **22** $6 + 8 =$ **23** $8 + 9 =$

ANSWERS

Page 3 • Lots of additions

1. 5 cats
   2 cats
   5 + 2 = 7
2. 1 more than 7 = 8
3. 1 more than 10 = 11
4. 4 + 3 = 7
5. 1 + 1 = 2
6. 2 + 1 = 3
7. 3 + 1 = 4
8. 4 + 1 = 5
9. 5 + 1 = 6
10. 6 + 1 = 7

Brodie's Fast Five
1. 6 + 2 = 8
2. 3 + 4 = 7
3. 7 + 1 = 8
4. 5 + 3 = 8
5. 10 + 1 = 11

Page 4 • Lots of subtractions

1. 7 birds
   5 birds
   7 − 2 = 5
2. 1 less than 7 = 6
3. 1 less than 10 = 9
4. 5 − 3 = 2
5. 10 − 1 = 9
6. 9 − 1 = 8
7. 8 − 1 = 7
8. 7 − 1 = 6
9. 6 − 1 = 5
10. 5 − 1 = 4

Page 5 • Addition problems

1. 8 bricks
2. 9 birds
   7 birds + 2 birds = 9 birds
   7 + 2 = 9

Page 6 • Subtraction problems

1. 6 cars
2. 9 peas − 3 peas = 6 peas
   9 − 3 = 6

Brodie's Fast Five
1. 7 − 4 = 3
2. 10 − 5 = 5
3. 6 − 6 = 0
4. 12 − 3 = 9
5. 9 − 8 = 1

Page 7 • Addition and subtraction

1. 7 + 2 = 9
2. 1 more than 9 = 10
3. 1 less than 6 = 5
4. 5 + 5 = 10
5. 9 − 3 = 6
6. 8 + 2 = 10
7. 7 − 4 = 3
8. 10 stars
   7 + 3 = 10
9. 10 − 7 = 3
10. 10 − 3 = 7

Brodie's Fast Five
1. 9 − 4 = 5
2. 8 − 3 = 5
3. 7 − 2 = 5
4. 6 − 1 = 5
5. 10 − 5 = 5

Page 8 • Progress Test 1

Addition
1. 6 + 2 = 8
2. 8 + 4 = 12
3. 0 + 7 = 7
4. 5 + 5 = 10
5. 9 + 3 = 12

Subtraction
6. 8 − 1 = 7
7. 9 − 5 = 4
8. 10 − 1 = 9
9. 6 − 0 = 6
10. 5 − 4 = 1
11. 9 cars − 2 cars = 7 cars
    9 − 2 = 7
12. 9 stars
    5 + 4 = 9

Page 9 • Lots of additions

1. 8 hats
   4 hats
   12 hats
   8 + 4 = 12
2. 1 more than 12 = 13
3. 1 more than 23 = 24
4. 7 + 6 = 13
5. 7 + 2 = 9
6. 8 + 2 = 10
7. 9 + 2 = 11
8. 10 + 2 = 12
9. 11 + 2 = 13
10. 12 + 2 = 14

Brodie's Fast Five
1. 7 + 5 = 12
2. 8 + 4 = 12
3. 6 + 6 = 12
4. 9 + 3 = 12
5. 10 + 2 = 12

Page 10 • Lots of subtractions

1. 10 biscuits
   8 biscuits
   10 − 2 = 8
2. 1 less than 12 = 11
3. 1 less than 18 = 17
4. 11 − 6 = 5
5. 13 − 2 = 11
6. 9 − 2 = 7
7. 14 − 2 = 12
8. 16 − 2 = 14
9. 2 − 2 = 0
10. 15 − 2 = 13

Brodie's Fast Five
1. 10 − 2 = 8
2. 17 − 1 = 16
3. 11 − 3 = 8
4. 12 − 2 = 10
5. 10 − 4 = 6

Page 11 • Let's make ten

0 + 10
10 + 0
1 + 9
9 + 1
2 + 8
8 + 2
3 + 7
7 + 3
4 + 6
6 + 4
5 + 5

0 + 10 = 10
10 + 0 = 10
1 + 9 = 10
9 + 1 = 10
2 + 8 = 10
8 + 2 = 10
3 + 7 = 10
7 + 3 = 10
4 + 6 = 10
6 + 4 = 10
5 + 5 = 10

Brodie's Fast Five
1. 12 + 2 = 14
2. 13 + 2 = 15
3. 11 + 4 = 15
4. 9 + 6 = 15
5. 10 + 9 = 19

Page 12 • Let's make two

10 − 8
9 − 7
8 − 6
7 − 5
6 − 4
5 − 3
4 − 2
3 − 1
2 − 0

10 − 8 = 2
9 − 7 = 2
8 − 6 = 2
7 − 5 = 2
6 − 4 = 2
5 − 3 = 2
4 − 2 = 2
3 − 1 = 2
2 − 0 = 2

Brodie's Fast Five
1. 12 − 4 = 8
2. 13 − 5 = 8
3. 11 − 11 = 0
4. 12 − 9 = 3
5. 15 − 3 = 12

Page 13 • Addition and subtraction

1. 14 + 2 = 16
2. 1 more than 19 = 20
3. 1 less than 21 = 20
4. 8 + 8 = 16
5. 20 − 3 = 17
6. 18 + 2 = 20
7. 16 − 4 = 12
8. 10 − 6 = 4
9. 10 + 6 = 16
10. 0 + 7
    1 + 6
    2 + 5
    3 + 4
    4 + 3
    5 + 2
    6 + 1
    7 + 0

Brodie's Fast Five
1. 19 − 4 = 15
2. 18 − 3 = 15
3. 17 − 2 = 15
4. 16 − 1 = 15
5. 20 − 5 = 15

Page 14 • Progress Test 2

Addition
1. 9 + 5 = 14
2. 8 + 7 = 15
3. 10 + 7 = 17
4. 15 + 5 = 20
5. 19 + 1 = 20

Subtraction
6. 20 − 1 = 19
7. 15 − 5 = 10
8. 14 − 5 = 9
9. 20 − 0 = 20
10. 20 − 4 = 16
11. 0 + 9
    1 + 8
    2 + 7
    3 + 6
    4 + 5
    5 + 4
    6 + 3
    7 + 2
    8 + 1
    9 + 0

0 + 9 = 9
1 + 8 = 9
2 + 7 = 9
3 + 6 = 9
4 + 5 = 9
5 + 4 = 9
6 + 3 = 9
7 + 2 = 9
8 + 1 = 9
9 + 0 = 9

12. 10 − 7
9 − 6
8 − 5
7 − 4
6 − 3
5 − 2
4 − 1
3 − 0

10 − 7 = 3
9 − 6 = 3
8 − 5 = 3
7 − 4 = 3
6 − 3 = 3
5 − 2 = 3
4 − 1 = 3
3 − 0 = 3

Page 15 • Adding using number lines

4 + 3 = 7
5 + 4 = 9
1 + 7 = 8
4 + 6 = 10
0 + 6 = 6

Brodie's Fast Five

1. 7 + 7 = 14
2. 8 + 8 = 16
3. 6 + 6 = 12
4. 9 + 9 = 18
5. 10 + 10 = 20

Page 16 • Subtracting using number lines

9 − 2 = 7
10 − 8 = 2
8 − 5 = 3
9 − 5 = 4
8 − 7 = 1

Brodie's Fast Five

1. 10 − 5 = 5
2. 18 − 1 = 17
3. 15 − 3 = 12
4. 20 − 2 = 18
5. 19 − 4 = 15

Page 17 • Let's make twelve

0 + 12
12 + 0
1 + 11
11 + 1
2 + 10
10 + 2
3 + 9
9 + 3
4 + 8
8 + 4
5 + 7
7 + 5

6 + 6
0 + 12 = 12
12 + 0 = 12
1 + 11 = 12
11 + 1 = 12
2 + 10 = 12
10 + 2 = 12
3 + 9 = 12
9 + 3 = 12
4 + 8 = 12
8 + 4 = 12
5 + 7 = 12
7 + 5 = 12
6 + 6 = 12

Brodie's Fast Five

1. 18 + 2 = 20
2. 14 + 5 = 19
3. 11 + 7 = 18
4. 9 + 8 = 17
5. 10 + 6 = 16

Page 18 • Let's make three

12 − 9
11 − 8
10 − 7
9 − 6
8 − 5
7 − 4
6 − 3
5 − 2
4 − 1
3 − 0

12 − 9 = 3
11 − 8 = 3
10 − 7 = 3
9 − 6 = 3
8 − 5 = 3
7 − 4 = 3
6 − 3 = 3
5 − 2 = 3
4 − 1 = 3
3 − 0 = 3

Brodie's Fast Five

1. 20 − 4 = 16
2. 20 − 8 = 12
3. 20 − 11 = 9
4. 20 − 9 = 11
5. 20 − 3 = 17

Page 19 • Addition and subtraction

1. 7 + 4 = 11
2. 3 more than 17 = 20
3. 3 less than 15 = 12
4. 10 + 10 = 20
5. 16 − 9 = 7
6. 20 + 5 = 25
7. 19 − 12 = 7
8. 14 + 9 = 23
9. 20 − 17 = 3
10. 0 + 8
8 + 0
1 + 7
7 + 1
2 + 6
6 + 2
3 + 5
5 + 3
4 + 4

Brodie's Fast Five

1. 21 − 4 = 17
2. 20 − 3 = 17
3. 15 − 2 = 13
4. 20 − 1 = 19
5. 14 − 5 = 9

Page 20 • Progress Test 3

Addition

1. 9 + 8 = 17
2. 12 + 7 = 19
3. 10 + 10 = 20
4. 15 + 6 = 21
5. 19 + 4 = 23

Subtraction

6. 20 − 8 = 12
7. 22 − 5 = 17
8. 21 − 6 = 15
9. 20 − 11 = 9
10. 23 − 4 = 19
11. 3 + 6 = 9
2 + 8 = 10
12. 10 − 4 = 6
9 − 7 = 2

Page 21 • Adding using number lines

14 + 5 = 19
10 + 8 = 18
11 + 9 = 20
4 + 10 = 14
12 + 8 = 20
9 + 11 = 20
6 + 11 = 17
7 + 9 = 16

Brodie's Fast Five

1. 7 + 7 = 14
2. 12 + 5 = 17
3. 14 + 6 = 20
4. 15 + 5 = 20
5. 6 + 10 = 16

Page 22 • Subtracting using number lines

14 − 7 = 7
16 − 5 = 11
18 − 9 = 9
19 − 7 = 12
17 − 4 = 13
20 − 11 = 9
19 − 11 = 8
15 − 9 = 6

Brodie's Fast Five

1. 20 − 3 = 17
2. 18 − 7 = 11
3. 19 − 5 = 14
4. 20 − 8 = 12
5. 17 − 8 = 9

Page 23 • Let's make thirteen

0 + 13
13 + 0
1 + 12
12 + 1
2 + 11
11 + 2
3 + 10
10 + 3
4 + 9

9 + 4
5 + 8
8 + 5
6 + 7
7 + 6

0 + 13 = 13
13 + 0 = 13
1 + 12 = 13
12 + 1 = 13
2 + 11 = 13
11 + 2 = 13
3 + 10 = 13
10 + 3 = 13
4 + 9 = 13
9 + 4 = 13
5 + 8 = 13
8 + 5 = 13
6 + 7 = 13
7 + 6 = 13

Brodie's Fast Five

1. 3 + 12 = 15
2. 4 + 15 = 19
3. 7 + 8 = 15
4. 6 + 11 = 17
5. 8 + 12 = 20

Page 24 • Let's make four

14 − 10
13 − 9
12 − 8
11 − 7
10 − 6
9 − 5
8 − 4
7 − 3
6 − 2
5 − 1
4 − 0

14 − 10 = 4
13 − 9 = 4
12 − 8 = 4
11 − 7 = 4
10 − 6 = 4
9 − 5 = 4
8 − 4 = 4
7 − 3 = 4
6 − 2 = 4
5 − 1 = 4
4 − 0 = 4

Brodie's Fast Five

1. 20 − 7 = 13
2. 20 − 12 = 8
3. 20 − 6 = 14
4. 20 − 11 = 9
5. 20 − 4 = 16

Page 25 • Addition and subtraction

1. 8 + 6 = 14
2. 3 more than 15 = 18
3. 3 less than 17 = 14
4. 6 + 7 = 13
5. 15 − 9 = 6
6. 12 + 5 = 17
7. 17 − 11 = 6
8. 8 + 9 = 17
9. 20 − 13 = 7
10. 0 + 11
11 + 0
1 + 10

10 + 1
2 + 9
9 + 2
3 + 8
8 + 3
4 + 7
7 + 4
5 + 6
6 + 5

Brodie's Fast Five

1. 19 − 4 = 15
2. 11 − 3 = 8
3. 17 − 2 = 15
4. 20 − 11 = 9
5. 13 − 5 = 8

Page 26 • Progress Test 4

1. 7 + 8 = 15
2. 12 − 7 = 5
3. 10 + 9 = 19
4. 15 − 6 = 9
5. 7 + 4 = 11
6. 20 − 9 = 11
7. 12 + 4 = 16
8. 17 − 6 = 11
9. 18 + 2 = 20
10. 20 − 14 = 6
11. 7 + 12 = 19
    9 + 7 = 16
12. 19 − 15 = 4
    20 − 14 = 6

Page 27 • Adding to find missing numbers

1. 6 + 4 = 10
2. 3 + 7 = 10
3. 9 + 1 = 10
4. 2 + 8 = 10
5. 4 + 6 = 10
6. 1 + 9 = 10
7. 5 + 5 = 10
8. 8 + 2 = 10
9. 7 + 3 = 10
10. 0 + 10 = 10

Brodie's Fast Five

1. 8 + 6 = 14
2. 12 + 7 = 19
3. 11 + 6 = 17
4. 13 + 5 = 18
5. 6 + 9 = 15

Page 28 • Subtracting to find missing numbers

1. 10 − 7 = 3
2. 10 − 1 = 9
3. 10 − 9 = 1
4. 10 − 0 = 10
5. 10 − 4 = 6
6. 10 − 3 = 7
7. 10 − 8 = 2
8. 10 − 6 = 4
9. 10 − 10 = 0
10. 10 − 5 = 5

Brodie's Fast Five

1. 20 − 4 = 16
2. 17 − 7 = 10
3. 19 − 12 = 7
4. 20 − 15 = 5
5. 17 − 11 = 6

Page 29 • Let's make fourteen

0 + 14
14 + 0
1 + 13
13 + 1
2 + 12
12 + 2
3 + 11
11 + 3
4 + 10
10 + 4
5 + 9
9 + 5
6 + 8
8 + 6
7 + 7

0 + 14 = 14
14 + 0 = 14
1 + 13 = 14
13 + 1 = 14
2 + 12 = 14
12 + 2 = 14
3 + 11 = 14
11 + 3 = 14
4 + 10 = 14
10 + 4 = 14
5 + 9 = 14
9 + 5 = 14
6 + 8 = 14
8 + 6 = 14
7 + 7 = 14

Brodie's Fast Five

1. 6 + 12 = 18
2. 5 + 15 = 20
3. 17 + 2 = 19
4. 12 + 7 = 19
5. 13 + 6 = 19

Page 30 • Let's make five

15 − 10
14 − 9
13 − 8
12 − 7
11 − 6
10 − 5
9 − 4
8 − 3
7 − 2
6 − 1
5 − 0

15 − 10 = 5
14 − 9 = 5
13 − 8 = 5
12 − 7 = 5
11 − 6 = 5
10 − 5 = 5
9 − 4 = 5
8 − 3 = 5
7 − 2 = 5
6 − 1 = 5
5 − 0 = 5

Brodie's Fast Five

1. 20 − 13 = 7
2. 20 − 9 = 11
3. 20 − 12 = 8
4. 20 − 8 = 12
5. 20 − 5 = 15

Page 31 • Addition and subtraction

1. 7 + 6 = 13
2. 12 + 5 = 17
3. 15 − 4 = 11
4. 8 + 7 = 15
5. 18 − 12 = 6
6. 13 + 5 = 18
7. 20 − 11 = 9
8. 7 + 9 = 16
9. 20 − 12 = 8
10. 15 − 9
    14 − 8
    13 − 7
    12 − 6
    11 − 5
    10 − 4
    9 − 3
    8 − 2
    7 − 1
    6 − 0

Brodie's Fast Five

1. 4 − 4 = 0
2. 16 − 3 = 13
3. 17 − 12 = 5
4. 20 − 13 = 7
5. 13 − 9 = 4

Page 32 • Progress Test 5

1. 7 + 5 = 12
2. 4 + 8 = 12
3. 2 + 10 = 12
4. 5 + 7 = 12
5. 9 + 3 = 12
6. 10 − 4 = 6
7. 10 − 1 = 9
8. 10 − 7 = 3
9. 10 − 2 = 8
10. 10 − 8 = 2
11. 14 + 6 = 20
12. 7 + 8 = 15
13. 16 − 9 = 7
14. 9 + 6 = 15
15. 16 − 9 = 7
16. 16 + 4 = 20
17. 20 − 8 = 12
18. 6 + 5 = 11

Page 33 • Adding to find missing numbers

1. 7 + 4 = 11
2. 2 + 9 = 11
3. 6 + 5 = 11
4. 1 + 10 = 11
5. 11 + 0 = 11
6. 5 + 6 = 11
7. 0 + 11 = 11
8. 8 + 3 = 11
9. 4 + 7 = 11
10. 3 + 8 = 11

Brodie's Fast Five

1. 18 + 2 = 20
2. 12 + 8 = 20
3. 11 + 4 = 15
4. 10 + 7 = 17
5. 11 + 9 = 20

Page 34 • Subtracting to find missing numbers

1. 11 − 6 = 5
2. 10 − 7 = 3
3. 11 − 2 = 9
4. 11 − 4 = 7
5. 9 − 5 = 4
6. 14 − 8 = 6
7. 10 − 1 = 9
8. 19 − 6 = 13
9. 19 − 4 = 15
10. 20 − 8 = 12

Brodie's Fast Five

1. 20 − 16 = 4
2. 19 − 4 = 15
3. 17 − 8 = 9
4. 18 − 15 = 3
5. 16 − 3 = 13

Page 35 • Let's make fifteen

0 + 15
15 + 0
1 + 14
14 + 1
2 + 13
13 + 2
3 + 12
12 + 3
4 + 11
11 + 4
5 + 10
10 + 5
6 + 9
9 + 6
7 + 8
8 + 7

0 + 15 = 15
15 + 0 = 15
1 + 14 = 15
14 + 1 = 15
2 + 13 = 15
13 + 2 = 15
3 + 12 = 15
12 + 3 = 15
4 + 11 = 15
11 + 4 = 15
5 + 10 = 15
10 + 5 = 15
6 + 9 = 15
9 + 6 = 15
7 + 8 = 15
8 + 7 = 15

Brodie's Fast Five

1. 7 + 9 = 16
2. 8 + 8 = 16
3. 14 + 3 = 17
4. 11 + 8 = 19
5. 9 + 9 = 18

Page 36 • Let's make six

16 – 10
15 – 9
14 – 8
13 – 7
12 – 6
11 – 5
10 – 4
9 – 3
8 – 2
7 – 1
6 – 0

16 – 10 = 6
15 – 9 = 6
14 – 8 = 6
13 – 7 = 6
12 – 6 = 6
11 – 5 = 6
10 – 4 = 6
9 – 3 = 6
8 – 2 = 6
7 – 1 = 6
6 – 0 = 6

Brodie's Fast Five

1. 20 – 11 = 9
2. 20 – 6 = 14
3. 20 – 14 = 6
4. 20 – 18 = 2
5. 20 – 15 = 5

Page 37 • Addition and subtraction

1. 12 + 4 = 16
2. 12 + 8 = 20
3. 15 – 8 = 7
4. 9 + 3 = 12
5. 19 – 12 = 7
6. 17 + 3 = 20
7. 20 – 13 = 7
8. 6 + 8 = 14
9. 20 – 2 = 18
10. 17 – 10
    16 – 9
    15 – 8
    14 – 7
    13 – 6
    12 – 5
    11 – 4
    10 – 3
    9 – 2
    8 – 1
    7 – 0

Brodie's Fast Five

1. 14 – 4 = 10
2. 16 – 15 = 1
3. 17 – 1 = 16
4. 20 – 18 = 2
5. 14 – 5 = 9

Page 38 • Progress Test 6

1. 5 + 7 = 12
2. 4 + 8 = 12
3. 7 + 5 = 12
4. 2 + 10 = 12
5. 1 + 11 = 12
6. 20 – 8 = 12
7. 20 – 1 = 19
8. 14 – 3 = 11
9. 17 – 7 = 10
10. 18 – 2 = 16

11. 12 + 5 = 17
12. 8 + 9 = 17
13. 16 – 5 = 11
14. 8 + 11 = 19
15. 20 – 9 = 11
16. 14 + 4 = 18
17. 17 – 8 = 9
18. 9 + 5 = 14

Page 39 • Adding one to any number

1. 9 + 1 = 10
2. 19 + 1 = 20
3. 29 + 1 = 30
4. 39 + 1 = 40
5. 49 + 1 = 50
6. 59 + 1 = 60
7. 69 + 1 = 70
8. 79 + 1 = 80
9. 89 + 1 = 90
10. 99 + 1 = 100
11. 22 + 1 = 23
12. 46 + 1 = 47
13. 50 + 1 = 51
14. 81 + 1 = 82
15. 88 + 1 = 89
16. 1 + 59 = 60
17. 1 + 97 = 98
18. 1 + 75 = 76
19. 1 + 43 = 44
20. 1 + 54 = 55

Brodie's Fast Five

1. 13 + 7 = 20
2. 4 + 8 = 12
3. 11 + 9 = 20
4. 6 + 6 = 12
5. 9 + 11 = 20

Page 40 • Subtracting one from any number

1. 10 – 1 = 9
2. 80 – 1 = 79
3. 30 – 1 = 29
4. 70 – 1 = 69
5. 100 – 1 = 99
6. 20 – 1 = 19
7. 60 – 1 = 59
8. 90 – 1 = 89
9. 40 – 1 = 39
10. 50 – 1 = 49
11. 68 – 1 = 67
12. 83 – 1 = 82
13. 50 – 1 = 49
14. 29 – 1 = 28
15. 92 – 1 = 91
16. 54 – 1 = 53
17. 75 – 1 = 74
18. 56 – 1 = 55
19. 97 – 1 = 96
20. 41 – 1 = 40

Brodie's Fast Five

1. 19 – 7 = 12
2. 17 – 9 = 8
3. 17 – 5 = 12
4. 15 – 8 = 7
5. 20 – 4 = 16

Page 41 • Let's make sixteen

0 + 16
16 + 0
1 + 15
15 + 1
2 + 14
14 + 2
3 + 13
13 + 3
4 + 12
12 + 4
5 + 11
11 + 5
6 + 10
10 + 6
7 + 9
9 + 7
8 + 8

0 + 16 = 16
16 + 0 = 16
1 + 15 = 16
15 + 1 = 16
2 + 14 = 16
14 + 2 = 16
3 + 13 = 16
13 + 3 = 16
4 + 12 = 16
12 + 4 = 16
5 + 11 = 16
11 + 5 = 16
6 + 10 = 16
10 + 6 = 16
7 + 9 = 16
9 + 7 = 16
8 + 8 = 16

Brodie's Fast Five

1. 7 + 9 = 16
2. 13 + 3 = 16
3. 2 + 14 = 16
4. 11 + 5 = 16
5. 9 + 7 = 16

Page 42 • Let's make seven

17 – 10
16 – 9
15 – 8
14 – 7
13 – 6
12 – 5
11 – 4
10 – 3
9 – 2
8 – 1
7 – 0

17 – 10 = 7
16 – 9 = 7
15 – 8 = 7
14 – 7 = 7
13 – 6 = 7
12 – 5 = 7
11 – 4 = 7
10 – 3 = 7
9 – 2 = 7
8 – 1 = 7
7 – 0 = 7

Brodie's Fast Five

1. 20 – 13 = 7
2. 13 – 6 = 7
3. 14 – 7 = 7
4. 16 – 9 = 7
5. 18 – 11 = 7

Page 43 • Addition and subtraction

1. 7 + 5 = 12
   12 – 7 = 5
   12 – 5 = 7
2. 6 + 9 = 15
   15 – 6 = 9
   15 – 9 = 6
3. 8 + 5 = 13
   13 – 8 = 5
   13 – 5 = 8
4. 9 + 3 = 12
   12 – 9 = 3
   12 – 3 = 9
5. 6 + 8 = 14
   14 – 6 = 8
   14 – 8 = 6
6. 9 + 7 = 16
   16 – 9 = 7
   16 – 7 = 9

Brodie's Fast Five

1. 14 – 6 = 8
2. 5 + 15 = 20
3. 18 – 1 = 17
4. 20 – 17 = 3
5. 12 – 5 = 7

Page 44 • Progress Test 7

1. 53 + 1 = 54
2. 68 + 1 = 69
3. 75 + 1 = 76
4. 28 + 1 = 29
5. 59 + 1 = 60
6. 80 + 1 = 81
7. 76 + 1 = 77
8. 1 + 89 = 90
9. 1 + 27 = 28
10. 1 + 33 = 34
11. 30 – 1 = 29
12. 70 – 1 = 69
13. 100 – 1 = 99
14. 50 – 1 = 49
15. 80 – 1 = 79
16. 70 – 1 = 69
17. 53 – 1 = 52
18. 74 – 1 = 73
19. 89 – 1 = 88
20. 91 – 1 = 90
21. 9 + 3 = 12
    12 – 9 = 3
    12 – 3 = 9
22. 6 + 8 = 14
    14 – 6 = 8
    14 – 8 = 6
23. 8 + 9 = 17
    17 – 8 = 9
    17 – 9 = 8